ANIMAL EXPLORERS

LOLA THE PLANT HUNTER

SHARON
RENTTA

ALISON
GREEN
BOOKS

Spring had sprung in the Arctic.
Lola and Grandpa Reggie yawned and stretched
and stepped out on the ice, where they found . . .

. . . one tiny flower.

"It's so pretty!" sighed Lola. "I wish there were more."
"There are!" said Grandpa Reggie. "Lots more.
You just have to know where to look."

Lola's grandpa had been a famous plant hunter and Lola loved hearing about his adventures.

"But there was just one special flower that I never found," sighed Grandpa. "The Singing Orchid! They say it's like a precious jewel, deep in the Amazon jungle.

"And it really does sing – imagine that! All the hummingbirds come flocking to hear it. I *so* wish I'd found it!"

Lola gazed at all of Grandpa's
drawings from his travels –
then she made a big decision.
"I'm going to find it for you!"
she said. "I'm going to be an
explorer, just like you!"

"That's my girl!" cried Grandpa.

From then on, Lola was a bear on a mission. She just needed to pack – but what should she take? Her friend, O'Hare, helped decide.

He said no to a lot of things.

They finally whittled it down to the bear essentials.

Hammock
Sardines.
sweets
loo roll - plenty!
notebooks
hat
sunglasses
flannel
map
binoculars
~~chocolate~~

Don't forget your toothbrush!

At last she was ready to set off for the Amazon.

Everyone said she was crazy – everyone except Grandpa.
"Good luck, my dear! I'm proud of you," he said, "even if you
don't find the Singing Orchid."

"But I will find it," said Lola. "I'm a bear on a mission."

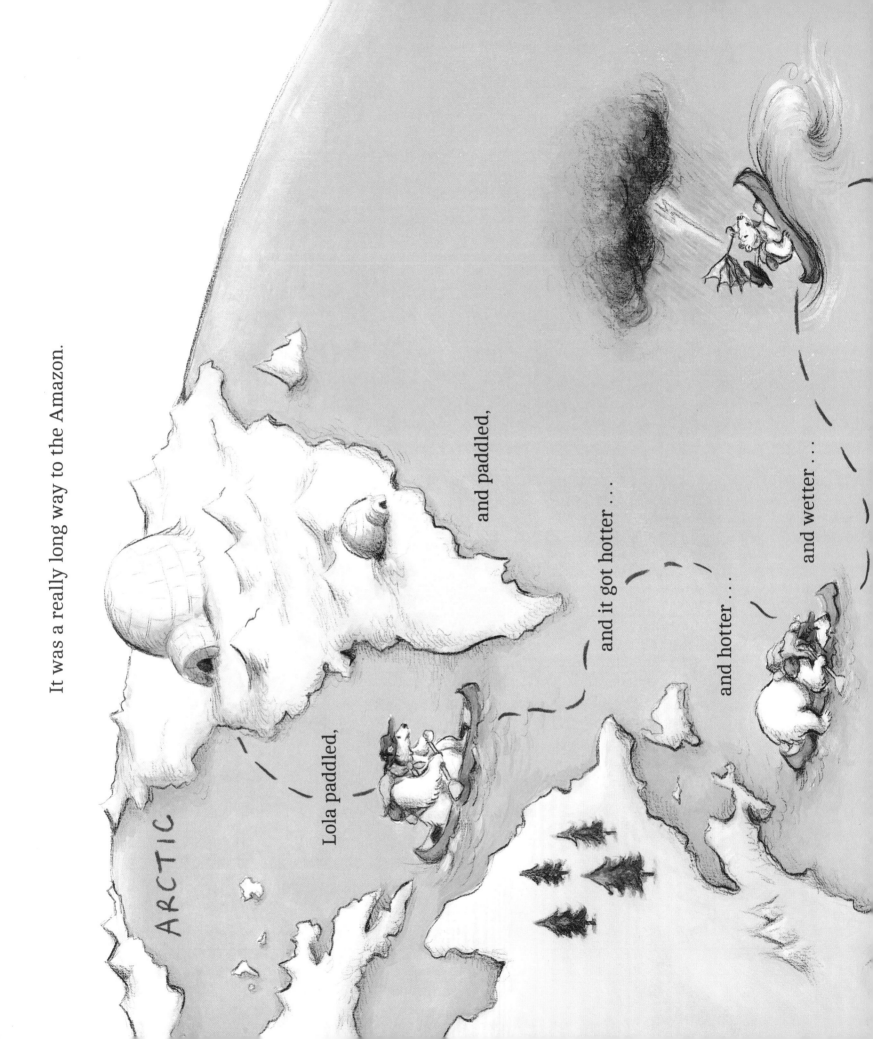

It was a really long way to the Amazon.

ARCTIC

Lola paddled,

and paddled,

and it got hotter . . .

and hotter . . .

and wetter . . .

and bumpier . . .

A shark tried to eat her canoe, so she bonked him on the nose with her paddle. "It'll take more than you to stop me," she said.

AMAZON RAINFOREST

At last she arrived, and . . .

. . . goodness! It was so green!
And so colourful!
And so noisy!

Chatter!

Shriek!

Squawk!

It was also very, **very big.**

How on earth would she find
one small orchid in all of this?
Lola took a deep breath, and
started looking.

For days and days she searched high . . .

. . . and low.

There were amazing flowers everywhere –

I've found flowers that are:

stinky

tiny

huge

scary

tasty

and even some that are houses.

but none of them could sing.

It was hot, hard work
for a polar bear.

There were too many bugs, too many
prickles and no ice anywhere – not even an ice-pop!
"But I won't give up," said Lola. "I'm a bear on a mission."

Just like Grandpa Reggie, she wrote up her
diary every night, and drew pictures
of everything she saw.

Then, one morning, Lola was woken early by huge raindrops falling on her nose. "Oh, no!" she sighed. "Rain! Well, I suppose it *is* the rainforest." She was about to put her hat on, when voices started shouting all around her.

RUN!!!!

THERE'S A STORM COMING!!!

Animals everywhere were running in panic.
As Lola fled after them, the sky grew dark and . . .

CRACK! FLASH!

The storm broke over their heads.
"Where are we running?" gasped Lola.
"Away!" panted an armadillo.
"Away from the river of . . .

Too late! They were swept
off their feet and whisked away
on a muddy torrent. They landed
in a sticky, dirty heap.

"Ow!"
grumbled
a gecko.

"Bleurgh!"
spluttered an
orangutan.

But, "Shhhh!" whispered Lola.
"Listen! Can you hear it?"

Hummingbird wings whirred overhead,
and they heard a sweet, strange music,
like lots of tiny little voices, singing.
Lola felt a thrill of excitement.

"Quick! I need to climb this tree!"
she cried. "And I'll need some help!"

Luckily, Lola had plenty of help.
She went up and up and up
and the singing grew louder
and louder until . . .

Hup!

. . . there they were!

Dozens of Singing Orchids! Lola couldn't believe her eyes
– or her ears. They were so beautiful. And they really were singing!

That night she sent
Grandpa Reggie a postcard.

"I did it, Grandpa!" she wrote.
"I found your Singing Orchid!

"And I think this might
just be the start of my
adventures!"

Lola's Singing Orchid really does exist.

It lives on pine trees in the rainforest of Peru, and its flowers give out a beautiful, high-pitched sound. This attracts hummingbirds which help spread the flowers' pollen.

Lola's story is inspired by some famous,
real-life plant hunters, too.

JEANNE BARET
(1740-1807)

DARING FRENCH BOTANIST AND EXPLORER

Though poor and with little education, Jeanne showed an early interest in plants. She later started working for a botanist called Philibert Commerçon, and he invited her to accompany him on an expedition as his assistant. Women weren't allowed on board ship, so Jeanne had to disguise herself as a boy.

Commerçon was often sick, so Jeanne did much of the work for him, collecting plants everywhere she went. She travelled from France to South America, Tahiti, Mauritius, and finally back to France – which made her the first woman ever to sail right round the world!

YNÉS MEXÍA
(1870-1938)

INTREPID MEXICAN-AMERICAN PLANT HUNTER

Ynés was born in Washington, DC, where her father was a Mexican diplomat. She spent much of her life in America, and discovered her love of plants late in life when, aged 51, she went on a botany field trip with a hiking club.

She soon began plant hunting all over Mexico and South America. It was dangerous work. Ynés was injured falling off a cliff in Mexico, and endured incredibly tough conditions while travelling up the Amazon.

Ynés was widely admired for her skills. She collected some 150,000 specimens, discovered many new species, and had dozens of plants named after her.

MARIANNE NORTH
(1830-1890)

VICTORIAN PAINTER IN THE JUNGLE

Marianne had two great loves: painting – and plants. To everyone's astonishment, she set off travelling on her own, so she could paint pictures of the exotic flowers she found. This was unheard of for a Victorian woman, and many people disapproved.

Marianne trekked to remote jungles and forests, from Borneo and Japan to South America and South Africa. Each time, she set up her easel and drew what she saw. Her detailed paintings show nearly 1000 plants, many of which were barely known to scientists. Her pictures can be seen today in a special gallery in the Royal Botanic Gardens at Kew.

For Renata,
who's always ready for adventure!

First published in the UK in 2020 by
Alison Green Books
An imprint of Scholastic Children's Books
Euston House, 24 Eversholt Street
London NW1 1DB
A division of Scholastic Ltd
www.scholastic.co.uk
London – New York – Toronto – Sydney
Auckland – Mexico City – New Delhi
Hong Kong
Designed by Zoë Tucker

HB ISBN: 978 1 407193 64 9
PB ISBN: 978 1 407193 65 6

1 3 5 7 9 8 6 4 2